"Some Of My Best Friends Are Jewish"

Gary Fink

"SO, STOP ME IF YOU'VE HEARD THIS ONE..."

BEFORE FINDING HIS TRUE CALLING, MOSES TRIES HIS HAND AT STAND-UP COMEDY.

FINKSTROM

TEMPLE BETH AM

Other Books By Finkstrom Productions:

FREQUENT FLYER FOIBLES by Gary Fink & Randy Evert
Illustrated by Jack Lindstrom
... What's so funny about flying on commercial airlines...**LOTS!**
Especially when you fly the comical skies aboard Knockwurst Airlines. This
full-color collection of hilarious cartoons is a must for all frequent flyers!

"You can count me among the people in the airline industry who
love your Frequent Flyer Foibles... outrageously funny!"
- Herbert D. Kelleher, Chairman of The Board,
President & Chief Executive Officer of Southwest Airlines

A RABBI CONFESSES by Rabbi Bob Alper
Illustrated by Jack Lindstrom
...The stand-up comedy of Rabbi Bob Alper in full-color cartoons!

"Rabbi Bob Alper is... a Jewish Bill Cosby... Take a trip to the land
comedy forgot."
- The New York Post

For information, write: **Finkstrom Productions**
16526 West 78th Street
Suite 340
Eden Prairie, MN 55346
1-800-86-COMIC

Library of Congress Catalog Card Number: 95-61726

ISBN: 1-888016-36-1
Printed in the USA

B eing Jewish is more than just being circumcised, neurotic, and buying "wholesale"... And as soon as I figure out what else it means... I'll get back to you!

In the meantime...
be a Mensch!

Presented to Temple Beth Am Library
in memory of
Annie Yasuda

by her Loving Grandparents
Rita & Jerry Frischer

"BETWEEN HIS DIARRHEA, CONSTIPATION, RECTAL HEMORRHOIDS AND CONSTANT FLATULENCE... ALL I WANT IS EQUAL TIME WITH HIS TOUCHAS."

11:45 P.M., SUNDAY NIGHT IN THE GINZBERG HOUSE... A FRIED RICE FART ACCIDENTALLY ESCAPES FROM THE TWISTED SHEETS.

TEMPLE ISRAEL, TOKYO, DEC. 7, 1941

SOL WEINBERG, RETIRED CONTRACTOR
FROM FLUSHING, N.Y., CONTINUES TO
UNDERCUT THE COMPETITION.

ECUMENICAL COUNCIL

I PLEDGE MORE EQUALITY FOR WOMEN...

I PLEDGE TO WORK TOWARD A SPIRITUAL RENAISSANCE...

I PLEDGE TO FIGHT BIGOTRY...

I PLEDGE $1,000.⁰⁰

FINKSTROM

COIN WASH

DELI

NOSH-A-RAMA

FINKSTROM

CLEANLINESS IS NEXT TO GODLINESS
...WHICH IS NEXT TO THE DELI!

MOUNT SINAI BOARD OF DIRECTOR'S MEETING.

WOODY WOODPECKER

EDDY BOJANGLES ROBINSON

SAMUEL F. B. MORSE

MONROE TAPPER, C.P.A.
N.Y.U., DOWNTOWN
CLASS OF '62.

FINKSTROM

"SOLLY'S HALF JEWISH AND HALF GYPSY...HE'S MADE
A FORTUNE FRANCHISING A CHAIN OF EMPTY STORES."

"YOU KNOW, SEYMOUR...RICH OR POOR...IT'S NICE TO HAVE MONEY."

SO...AT LEAST HE DOESN'T HAVE TO WORRY
ABOUT CONSTIPATION ANYMORE.

I'M ASKING YOU AARON... IS THIS A PERFECT PLACE
FOR A HOSPITAL, OR WHAT?

FUNNY... YOU DON'T LOOK JEWISH!

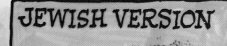

HANNAH BELLE STEIN CROSSING THE ALPS.

GINSBERG OF THE F.B.I. BLOWS HIS COVER.

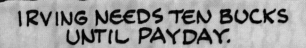

"SOME OF MY BEST FRIEND IS JEWISH."